DINOPALS

The Dino-mite Band

by Wiley Blevins
Illustrated by Emma Dodd

SCHOLASTIC INC.
Cartwheel
·B·O·O·K·S·®

New York   Toronto   London   Auckland   Sydney
Mexico City   New Delhi   Hong Kong   Buenos Aires

I am T Rex.

I can play the guitar.

I am Cam.

I can play the piano.

I am Meg.

Bang.

Bang.

Bang.

I can play the drums.

I am Al.

I can sing.

We play in a band.